# Garfield

## Guide
## To
# HEALTHY LIVING

### JIM DAVIS

RAVETTE PUBLISHING

This edition first published by Ravette Publishing Limited 1999.

Printed and bound for Ravette Publishing Limited,
Unit 3, Tristar Centre
Star Road, Partridge Green
West Sussex RH13 8RA
by STIGE, Italy

ISBN: 1 85304 972 7

5

9

10

12

13

15

16

18

20

21

22

23

24

27

28

29

30

52

93

34

35

36

37

39

45

46

49

50

52

53

54

55

56

57

58

59

60

61

62